708

The UNTOLD

ADVENTURES

SANTA of CLAUS

 OGDEN NASH

illustrated by Walter Lorraine

LITTLE, BROWN AND COMPANY

BOSTON   TORONTO

Books for young readers by Ogden Nash

PARENTS KEEP OUT: Elderly Poems for Youngerly Readers

THE CHRISTMAS THAT ALMOST WASN'T

CUSTARD THE DRAGON

CUSTARD THE DRAGON AND THE WICKED KNIGHT

THE NEW NUTCRACKER SUITE AND OTHER INNOCENT VERSES

THE ADVENTURES OF ISABEL

THE UNTOLD ADVENTURES OF SANTA CLAUS

Library of Congress Catalog Card No. 63-14237

First Edition

*Published simultaneously in Canada
by Little, Brown & Company (Canada) Limited*

Printed in the United States of America

People think they know all about Santa Claus,
But I happen to know they don't,
Because —
Well, because of a story that reached my ear
Which sheds new light on the saint's career.
People think his journeys sail along
As smooth and sweet as a Christmas song,
With nothing to do but chuckle and smile
And chirp to the reindeer once in a while,
And nothing to worry about at all
But a gift too large for a chimney too small.
They think that his life is one long Ho-ho!,
But they're wrong,
And I'll tell you how I know.

It was one of those wintery-smelling nights,
And the sky was alive with northern lights,
Flickering lights,
Glimmering lights,
Quivery,
Shivery,
Shimmering lights,
Wavering,
Trembling,
Rippling,
Drifting,
A vast kaleidoscope softly shifting.

I was out for a lonely midnight stroll
Watching the dazzling sky unroll,
Craning my neck,
Now to,
Now fro,

When I heard a thump in the soft new snow,
And there,
Like a bug on a charlotte russe,
Lay a little man the size of a goose.

I picked him up,
And I brushed his clothes,
And I wiped the snow from his turned-up nose,
And I asked him, as I carried him home,
Was he an elf,
Or was he a gnome?
But whether a gnome
Or whether an elf,
I still don't know,
For he didn't, himself.
I fed him on peanut butter and jelly
And good hot chocolate to warm his belly.
At last,
Convinced of his own survival,
He gave an account of his strange arrival.

A workman he was of good St. Nick's;
He painted the stripes on candy sticks.
Often, he said, on winter nights

He liked to
Slide
On
The
Northern
Lights.
This time he slid in a slippery trough,
And before he knew it,
He slid
Right
Off.

I settled him down on a cozy couch
With pillows arranged to soothe each ouch,
And presently,
After a decent pause,
I began to ask about Santa Claus.
Slowly at first,
Then ever faster,
He told me tales of his jolly master,
Which now without any more ado
I take pleasure in passing on to you.

There is a picture,
There is a painting,
With which I am sure you need no acquainting,
A canvas that every schoolboy knows
Of a gallant boat amid icy floes.
It thrills the blood like a trumpet's blare —
Washington Crossing the Delaware.
It's a pity the artist
Wasn't
There.
He had pondered time and time again
On General George and his ragged men;
His imagination was vivid, no doubt,
But he left an important figure out,
So it's time that you learned how Santa Claus
Furthered the Continental cause.

Christmas night of 1776.
The Christmas candles were smoldering wicks,
And Santa, having circled the globe,
Was weary and worn as poor old Job,
With never a thought in his nodding head
But a good warm meal and a good warm bed,
And the reindeer forgot their steaming coats
As they dreamt of the stable a-brim with oats.
The faithful sleigh could be put to rest,
Now empty as last year's robin's nest,
For the letters from all good girls and boys
Had been answered with jolly Christmas toys.

As they dropped toward the Pole
Like a burned-out rocket
Santa put his hand in his jacket pocket.
"Heavens to Betsy, my goose is cooked!
Here's a letter I must have overlooked!"
He ripped the envelope, read the note,
Which I'll do my humble best to quote.
Addressed to Santa Claus, Esquire,
"Sir," it began, "my need is dire.
My men are freezing in tattered rags,
They are eating their boots and saddlebags.
Their hearts are strong but their bodies fail,
It seems that tyranny must prevail.
And yet, though hope has almost died,
One victory would turn the tide;
Then hopeful men, as well as free,

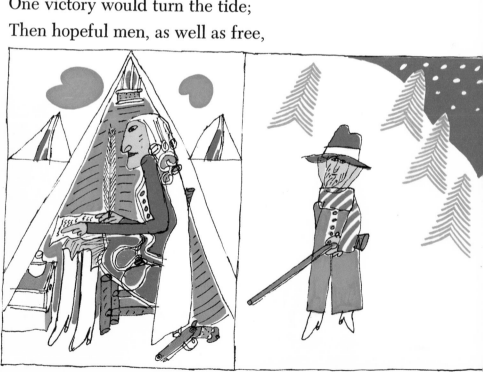

Would sweep the invader back to sea.
Therefore, Sir,
For Liberty's sake,
A lesser liberty I take,
And pray that you will send us swift
A victory for our Christmas gift.
I now remain
As I begun,
Your humble servant,
G. Washington.
P.S. You may perhaps recall
A gift you brought me when I was small.
Boy never saw a toy to match it,
That sharp and shiny
Handy
Hatchet."

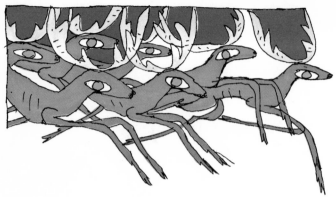

Then what a hustle
And what a stir!
The sleigh swung round
With a whizz and whirr.
Saint and reindeer
Forgot fatigue,
Flashing ever southward,
League on league,
Till they landed on what
At a future date
Would be the second United State.
There were the soldiers breaking camp
In tattered uniforms chill and damp.
And there,
Drawn up at the river bank,
A fleet of boats in a wobbling rank.
What kind of boats?
Any kind of boat,
Any sort of contraption that would float.
How the well-fed Hessians would have laughed
At thought of a threat from these clumsy craft!

The Americans stumbled through the dark
At the whispered order to embark.
In the foremost boat was a silhouette
That even a saint would never forget:
Against the sky, in bold relief,
The form of the stern Commander-in-Chief.
Hushing the reindeer's weary moans,
Santa Claus bade them rest their bones,
And then,
In one magical giant stride,

Took his place in the bow at the General's side.
So light was he,
Though so round and fat,
That he lit as soft as a spectral cat.
He remarked,
As he touched the General's shoulder,
"You're the boy I knew, just a trifle older."
Washington murmured in breath of frost,
"If the Hessians hear us, our cause is lost."

Said Santa,
"Christmas is almost gone,
But victory shall be yours ere dawn.
Just hark to your patron old and wise,
And we'll give the rascals a double surprise."
He whispers low in the General's ear
As the fires on the Jersey shore appear.
The ice cakes batter against the scow,
But he stands like a figurehead in the prow.

The Hessians are keeping Christmas still,
They are making merry with right good will,
Rollicking, frolicking, hiccuping chaps,
Full of pumpernickel
And goose
And Schnapps.

So sure of themselves are these arrogant gentry
They have set out only a single sentry.
As he is pacing the frozen shore
He hears the splash of a stealthy oar.
He hollers
(In Hessian),
"Who goes there?"

And points his gun at the Delaware;
He is just about to discharge the musket
When Santa's tactics his wits obfuscate.
Out of the murk there looms a boat,
And bright in the bow, a scarlet coat,
The scarlet worn by the lads who join
Under Howe or Gentleman Johnny Burgoyne.
"The wictorious British,"
The sentry thinks,
"Mit our Christmas vages in gold that clinks."
He stands at attention
Ramrod stiff;
The Americans pour from barge and skiff,

And quicker than you could salt a cod
Twelve hundred Hessians cry "Kamerad!"
Washington turns to the rosy saint,
The figure the painter forgot to paint.
"This time, my friend, and thanks to thee,
We have chopped down more than a cherry tree!"

By now my elf —
Or was he my gnome? —
Was warm and cozy,
And quite at home.
I saw it filled him with pride and glee
To instruct an ignorant mortal like me.
He blossomed, he bloomed,
Like a pink azalea,
And asked
Had I ever heard of Australia.
He was quite toplofty,
And, I may add,
He was also annoyed when I said I had.
He continued as if he hadn't heard,
"It's the home of the Kookaburra bird,
Where you talk to the bushmen,

Or aborigines,
In pidgin English,
Which I call pidgenese.
There you'll find the koala,
And wallaby too,
A sort of a kind of a kangaroo.

It's where the friendly city of Perth
Cheered Colonel Glenn with the lights of earth,
And it lies,
To make my lesson complete,
Some thousands of miles beneath your feet."

I gave the coals on the hearth a jog;
"Enough," I said, "of this travelogue.
Proceed, if you please,
To whatever event
Occurred on this marvelous continent."

"I thank you," said he,
"For your hospitality,
Dispensed with prodigious prodigality.
I miss, however,
A certain civility,
I regret the absence
Of proper humility.
But since broadmindedness is my creed
I shall now,
As you graciously put it,
Proceed."

Think back to a Christmas some years ago
When deliveries ran a trifle slow,
And children complained to their helpless mothers
Of presents clearly designed for others.

Tonight,

For the first time anywhere, I

Will reveal the how and where and why.

Santa was in the antipodes,

Soaring as sweetly as you please,

When one of the reindeer pulled up lame,

A reindeer I hesitate to name,

Only noting that Dancer,
For some time back,
Had been known as a
Hy-
Po-
Chon-
Dri-
Ac.

Here's a pretty pickle!
What's to be done?
There's a race against the clock to run.
Santa halted beneath a eucalyptus,
And he groaned, 'The clock will have soon outstripped us,
And children will weep
From attic to basement
Unless I can find a swift replacement."

He was scratching his head
And tugging his beard,
When a kangaroo
Up and volunteered.
Never had been
Such a friend in need;

Santa hitched him beside his complaining steed —
The kangaroo gave a mighty bound,
And the ill-matched team flew off the ground.
He leaped like a frog
Off a lily pad

Or a ballet dancer
Gone raving mad,
Like a tiddledywink,
Or a whooping Sioux,
And especially like —
A kangaroo.
They popped from the earth
Like toast from a toaster,
Then swooped and looped
Like a roller coaster;

Dipping,

Swerving,

Hairpin curving,

Somersaulting and topsy-turving.

Swollen with pride

In his own kind action,

The kangaroo strove to give satisfaction.

He slapped his tail

On the Little Bear,

And cleared the moon with inches to spare.

The sleigh was like a boy at the tip
In a vigorous game of crack-the-whip.
And after a specially splendid hop
The bottom would often turn up on top.
Oh, what a jumble
In Santa's sack
As it bounced about like a jumping-jack!
Once it had been such an orderly space,
Every toy had its special place,
A bug in a rug
Was never snugger;
Now all was awry and huggermugger,

Littery,
Cluttery,
Joggledy,
Jiggledy,
Horridly squiggledy higgledy-piggledy.
Trains and trumpets together fell,
Bicycles, tricycles,
All pell-mell.
Ice skates, roller skates,
Helter-skelter,
Mrs. Noah
Tossed from her shelter.

Tumbling dolls and teddy bears
Played willy-nilly at musical chairs;
Nothing was in its proper location,
'Twas a scene of
Kangaruination.

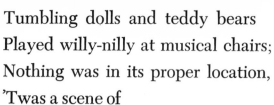

Where, you may ask,
Had Santa gone?
He was busy simply hanging on.
The reindeer couldn't tell head from hoof,
What was cellar and what was roof.

Before their eyes
Were nothing but specks
As their collars pressed against their necks.
Indeed, they might truly have choked to death,
Had Dancer not finally caught his breath.

He gasped as he'd never gasped before,
"I think —
That I'm —
Not — lame — any — more!"
Santa roared an overpowering "Whoa!"

Then headed the sleigh for the ground below.
They paused to unhitch the kangaroo,
Who told them he'd like to enter a zoo,
And by way of saying farewell he trilled a
Kangaroo version of "Waltzing Matilda."

Dancer firmly stated,
There and then,
That since he would never go lame again,
Santa needn't resort,
On his account,
To a grizzly bear
Or a catamount.

Said Santa, "My pack is in a mess,
But it's got to remain that way, I guess.
There's no time to rearrange the toys,
So there'll be some astonished girls and boys.
I'll never know which was meant for who
Because of that kindly kangaroo!"
So once again they took to the air
And completed their mission to everywhere
With exactly
Half
A second
To spare,
And Santa remarked,
With a smile sublime,
"I'm not only St. Nick,
I'm the Nick of time!"

And now my gnome —
Or was he my elf? —
Was really getting above himself,
Like a little girl
Who taunts her beau,
Crying, "I know something you don't know!"
But his scorn of me
Never grew so utter
That he scorned my jelly and peanut butter.
He gave his lips a perfunctory wipe,
Then helped himself to my favorite pipe,
And filling it from my tobacco pouch,
He spoke through the smoke that wreathed the couch.

Many silly people, because they hear
That Christmas comes only once a year,
Think Santa only goes out to drive **U. S.1370405**
One night of three hundred and sixty-five,
And the other three hundred and sixty-four
Plays at shuttlecock and battledore;
That he passes his time at checkers or darts,
Or a friendly hand of Old Maid or Hearts.
The proof of their folly is more than ample;
Allow me to give you a simple sample
Of how he has to roll up his sleeves
And buckle down between Christmas Eves.
You know how early, and more's the pity,
Christmas begins in the modern city;
In some, through a custom quaint and quirky,
Even before the Thanksgiving turkey.

As you walk the streets in late November
The chestnuts roast on the glowing ember,
And a faint sweet smell from the bursting husk
Tickles your nose in the early dusk.
Carols chime from the darkening spires,
And the shops resound with recorded choirs,

And on every corner a Santa Claus
Is collecting funds for a worthy cause.
Thus every make-believe Kriss Kringle
Has a Christmas bell to clang and jingle,
And a shiny caldron to catch the eye
And attract the coins of the passer-by.

Santa feels an affection warm
For these mortals who don his uniform,
And brave the winter winds to ensure
Food and clothes for the homeless poor.
And as a result of this affection
He often makes a tour of inspection,
To see for himself, mid the Christmas throng,
How his counterparts are getting along.
He was walking, not many years ago,
The streets of a city that well you know.
He attracted no attention, because
Every corner boasted its Santa Claus.
But sudden — and what could be forlorner? —
He perceived a Santa Clausless corner.
Sad on the tripod the caldron swung,
And the bell on the sidewalk lay unrung.

"Goodness gracious!" exclaimed St. Nick.
"This Santa must have been taken sick."
He seized the bell and gave such a jingle

That it set the pedestrians all a-tingle,
Ever louder and merrier did he rock it
Till it charmed the money from every pocket.
Citizens hurried from all around,

Lured by the irresistible sound;
They filled the caldron a dozen times
With glistening nickels and quarters and dimes,
And the ever-mounting overflow
Spilled in a heap on the curb below.
But now there was heard a footstep loud;
A policeman shouldered through the crowd.

He gripped the saint by the ringing arm,
And blew his whistle to sound the alarm.
"I know the Santa who works this corner,
You're much unshavener, much unshorner.

Where is your license? Where's your permit?
Who do you work for, and who'll confirm it?
What are you up to? What's your game?
Where's your residence? What's your name?"
Said Santa sadly, "I'd better withhold it;
You wouldn't believe me if I told it."
The policeman grunted, "It's my belief
That you're nothing more than a common thief!
A thief too steeped in sin for shame,
A thief who steals in charity's name!"

From the crowd there came an ominous mumble
That swelled to an angry snarling rumble.
"Hanging's too easy for him by far,
Let's give him a dose of feathers and tar!"
Santa realized he was treading on eggs;
He ducked through the huge policeman's legs;

He scattered the mob from wall to wall,
And was off like a scarlet cannon ball.
At the nearest corner he made a pause

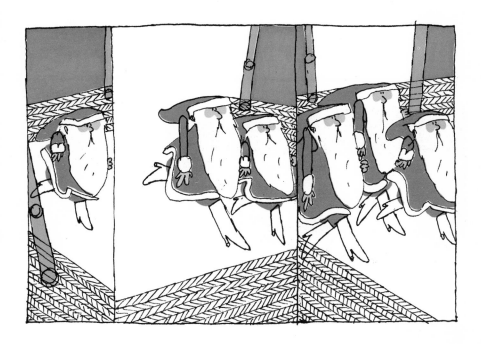

To hook on to that startled Santa Claus,
And at each new corner he grabbed another,
Till you couldn't distinguish one from t'other;
Two score, *three* score stout old Santas

Sprinted like youthful Atalantas;
They ran, though the only inducement spoken
Was St. Nicholas calling, "The dam has broken!"

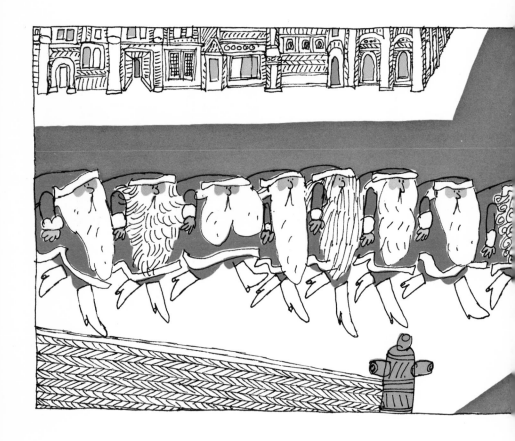

The avenue, when at last they stopped,
Looked as though a bag of cherries had popped.
The pursuers are stumped; if they want their fun

They must tar and feather all or none.
It's impossible,
Just though they think their cause is,

To pick Santa Claus
From the Santa Clauses.

The real one clucked, and in speedy answer
Swoop the reindeer, led by the penitent Dancer.
"Hereafter," he vowed as he took his leave,
"I'll confine my good deeds to Christmas Eve!"

Said my guest, "I could more tales unfold
To make your very blood run cold,
But of Santa's adventures from year to year
The preceding may give you some idear,"
At which I guessed he was not from Dixie,
But a Yankee gnome or elf or pixie.
"And now," he said, "I must quit your palace,
I see my aurora borealis,
And it may not come this way again
For five more years, or maybe ten,
And whether I'm pixie, elf, or gnome,
I know that I must hurry home."
He waved his hand in a gesture weird,
As he walked through the door and disappeared.
I'm a practical man, from fancy exempt;
I'd laugh this off as a dream I dreamt —
But my walking stick,
Once of ash wood plain,
Is now a gaudy candy cane.